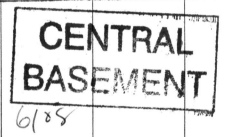

The Count of Luxembourg

(Operetta in 3 Acts)

Original book and lyrics by

A. M. WILLNER and R. BODANZKY

Music by

FRANZ LEHÁR

Translated and adapted by

ERIC MASCHWITZ

Music arranged and adapted by

BERNARD GRUN

Application for a licence to perform this Operetta
must be addressed to

GLOCKEN VERLAG LTD.
10-16 RATHBONE STREET
LONDON
W1P 2BJ

Reprinted 1975

THE COUNT OF LUXEMBOURG

SCENES

The action of the Play takes place
in Paris in the year 1910

THE COUNT OF LUXEMBOURG

CHARACTERS

RENÉ	*the spendthrift Count of Luxembourg*
BRISSARD	*a pastry-cook, turned artist*
JULIETTE	*his reluctant model*
SAVILLE	*an aspiring painter, later a bar tender*
MARCHAND	*an aspiring sculptor, later a journalist*
THE GRAND DUKE BASIL	*a Russian aristocrat*
MENTCHIKOFF ⎱ PAVLOVITCH ⎰	*his secret agents*
M'SIEU PELEGRIN	*a Registrar of Marriages*
ANGÈLE DIDIER	*an Opera Singer, beloved of the Grand Duke*
MOUCHOIR	*her major-domo*
M'SIEU CAZENOVE	*an ardent dance partner*
HEAD PORTER	*of the Grand Hotel*
JO-JO	*his assistant, a very small page boy*
THE PRINCESS KOKOSOV	*a visitor from Moscow*

Carnival Revellers, Guests of Angèle, Habitués of the
Champagne Garden, Dancers, Waitresses, etc., etc.

THE COUNT OF LUXEMBOURG

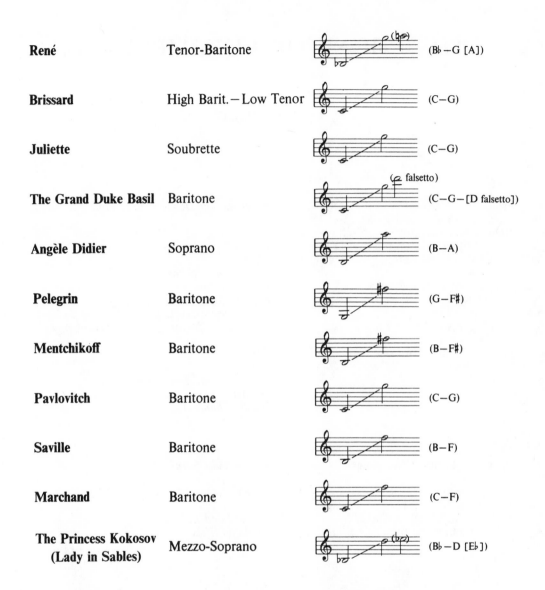

René	Tenor-Baritone	(B♭–G [A])
Brissard	High Barit.–Low Tenor	(C–G)
Juliette	Soubrette	(C–G)
The Grand Duke Basil	Baritone	(C–G–[D falsetto])
Angèle Didier	Soprano	(B–A)
Pelegrin	Baritone	(G–F♯)
Mentchikoff	Baritone	(B–F♯)
Pavlovitch	Baritone	(C–G)
Saville	Baritone	(B–F)
Marchand	Baritone	(C–F)
The Princess Kokosov (Lady in Sables)	Mezzo-Soprano	(B♭–D [E♭])

THE ORCHESTRA

The minimum combination for an effective performance is: Flute, Oboe, 1st and 2nd B♭ Clarinets, 1st and 2nd Trumpets, 1st Trombone, Percussion and Strings. Thereafter instruments should be added in the following order: 2nd Trombone, Bassoon, 1st and 2nd Horns and Harp. The work is liberally cued. In the absence of the Oboe the 1st Trumpet should play these cues muted. Oboe cues are doubled in Flute and Clarinet parts where practicable and Horn and Bassoon cues appear in Cello, Trombone and Trumpet parts. It is emphasised that a complete String section should be used but Clarinet parts contain many essential cues to be played in the absence of a Viola. The 1st Violin has all important melody cues throughout. The Vocal Score carries instrumentation marks for the Musical Director's assistance.

THE COUNT OF LUXEMBOURG

MUSIC PLOT

THE COUNT OF LUXEMBOURG

Operetta in 3 Acts

Original Book and Lyrics by
A. M. WILLNER and R. BODANZKY

Translated and adapted by
ERIC MASCHWITZ

Music by
FRANZ LEHÁR

Arranged and adapted by
BERNARD GRUN

OVERTURE

(On Lehár Motives)

4

9

10 Allegro non troppo

11 Moderato

6

Act I
No. 1. PROLOGUE
(Rene and Chorus)

8

Count of Luxembourg

10

Count of Luxembourg

12

Count of Luxembourg

RENÉ *(spoken)* "Salut, mes amis!" REVELLERS *(spoken)* "Salut!"

14

Count of Luxembourg

16

Attaca No. 1a

No. 1a. CARNIVAL - MARCH and BALLET
(Chorus)

18

Count of Luxembourg

Cho.

Pier - rot_____ where ev -'ry clown is a lov- er and a he - ro_____ to - mor- row

Pier - rot_____ where ev -'ry clown is a lov- er and a he - ro_____ to - mor- row

of Col - um - bine_____ and world of Pier - rot_____ where ev -'ry clown_____

of Col - um - bine_____ and world of Pier - rot_____ where ev -'ry clown_____

Cho.

may be the day for re - gret-ting things and yet to night let your heart have

may be the day for re - gret-ting things and yet to night let your heart have

_____ is just a he - ro_____ re - gret-ting things_____ let your heart have

_____ is just a he - ro_____ re - gret-ting things_____ let your heart have

7

Cho.

wings !_____

wings !_____

wings !_____

wings !_____

W.W.
Brass   **7**

f marcato

Stgs.

Count of Luxembourg

TUTTI

ff

rit.

8 **Grandioso**
Chorus

Pa - ris at Car - ni - val is play - time_____ when hap-py fools turn the night-time in -to

Pa - ris at Car - ni - val is play-time_____ when hap-py fools turn the night-time in - to

Pa - ris at Car - ni - val is play - time_____ when hap-py fools turn the night-time in - to

Pa - ris at Car - ni - val is play - time_____ when hap-py fools turn the night-time into

8 **Grandioso**

ff

day - time_____ Ah !_____

CHO.
day - time_____ Ah !_____

day - time_____ It's just a wild world of mad make be-lieve_____ a wan-d'ring

day - time_____ It's just a wild world of mad make be-lieve_____ a wan-d'ring

Count of Luxembourg

22

9

Attaca No. 1b

No. 1b. REPRISE and RECITATIVE
(Juliette, Brissard and Chorus)

Car-ni-val, crazy day of Car-ni-val, Hail the Feast of Fools, Hail the God of Wine, Fol-ly

makes the rules, Reason's out of line! Car-ni-val, that's the way of Car-ni-val, Let the

Count of Luxembourg

24

Fade out as Revellers exeunt.

mus - ic sound, let the wel - kin ring, fools in fol - ly drowned laugh and love and sing.

CHO.

mus - ic sound, let the wel - kin ring, fools in fol - ly drowned laugh and love and sing.

mus - ic sound, let the wel - kin ring, fools in fol - ly drowned laugh and love and sing.

mus - ic sound, let the wel - kin ring, fools in fol - ly drowned laugh and love and sing.

CURTAIN The Studio of Brissard

2 Allegretto Brissard

The dev - il take the whole af - fair, wast - ing our mon-ey, wast-ing

BRIS.

time! What is the land - lord going to say?

3

BRIS.

Land - lord? Who cares for him?!

No. 2. "Two Millionaires on the Rue d'Amour" - Duet
(Juliette and Brissard)

CUE: you *do* make it sound so attractive!

Count of Luxembourg

28

JUL. steal up the stair, My way and your way we'll tip - toe on air, Count - ing our

BRIS. steal up the stair, My way and your way we'll tip - toe on air, Count - ing our

JUL. bless - ings we'll be for sure Two million - aires on the Boul' - vard d'A - mour ! -mour !

BRIS. bless - ings we'll be for sure Two million - aires on the Boul' - vard d'A - mour ! -mour !

Attaca No. 2 a
Count of Luxembourg

No. 2a. STREET MUSIC and ENTRANCE of REVELLERS
(Chorus)

JULIETTE: It will be Heaven. I can't wait to sign on the dotted line.

BRISSARD: Sign? You mean the lease?

JULIETTE: Not a bit of it—the Marriage Register!

Tempo di Marcia BRISSARD (*aghast*): Wha-at?

JULIETTE: Have you forgotten, sweetheart . . . no marriage, no Venus! Remember, I'm so *bourgeois!*

Entrance of Revellers.

Chorus

Sing, sing the Car-ni-val Song speed-ing the tip-sy hours a-

Sing, sing the Car-ni-val Song speed-ing the tip-sy hours a-

Sing, sing the Car-ni-val Song speed-ing the tip-sy hours a-

Sing, sing the Car-ni-val Song speed-ing the tip-sy hours a-

Count of Luxembourg

Count of Luxembourg

No. 3. "SURPRISE"
(Juliette and Chorus)

CUE: I now declare this most unexpected banquet open !

1 In this world of stress and strife you will rea-
2 May be this ro-man-tic theme here is out of

-lise there's no lov-lier thing in life than a real sur-
place if we dreamed a hun-gry dream That was no dis-

-prise. When the land is lost in snow and the days are sad and slow,
-grace. We were star-ving for a feast just like an-y jun-gle beast,

Count of Luxembourg

34

Count of Luxembourg

Count of Luxembourg

Count of Luxembourg

8 Tempo di Valse

Count of Luxembourg

As to and fro you wan – – der in search of dreams come

Count of Luxembourg

12

No. 4. ENTRANCE OF RENE - REPRISE
(Renè and Chorus)

Count of Luxembourg

No. 4a. EXIT
(Rene and Chorus)

CUE : . . . . sing to keep my courage up.

Count of Luxembourg

No. 5. "I'M SO IN LOVE"

(Basil, Pavlovitch, Mentchikoff and Pelegrin)

CUE : I am not really quite myself.

48

Count of Luxembourg

Count of Luxembourg

52

Count of Luxembourg

No. 6. "A COOL HALF MILLION FRANCS"
(Rene, Basil, Pavlovitch, Mentchikoff and Pelegrin)

CUE: the "Countess of Luxembourg" will divorce you and—voila!

56

3 a tempo *(Business)*

RENE: Would we watch him through the bars? ___

RENE: **Animato** Though it may be crude to ___ touch on, *Vln.* what's the blot on her es - cutch-eon?

RENE: *rit.* If there's something ra - ther sha-dy, I can do with-out the la - dy! *Meno*

RENE: Is that so? Then you swear she's all right?

Basil: Is that so? Oh, no no! All right? Sheer de-light!

Pavlovitch: Is that so? Oh, no no! ___ All right? Sheer de-light!

Mentchikoff: Is that so? Oh, no no! ___ All right? Sheer de-light!

Pelegrin: Is that so? Oh, no no! ___ All right? Sheer de-light!

Count of Luxembourg

No. 6a. "I'M SO IN LOVE" REPRISE
(Basil)

CUE: Don't cross the cheque.

No. 7. "FANCY FREE"
(Angèle)

CUE: A Carnival affair if there ever was one.

I'm to be a bride to-day, join the ma-rried clan, though what he's like I

can-not say, ex-cept that he's a man. For my fate...

Count of Luxembourg

No. 8. FINALE ACT I
(Full Company)

CUE: Sure that there is no nonsense.

Allegretto moderato

RENÉ AND ANGÈLE: No peeping?

Rene

Con-grat-u - la-tions, chere Madame,

Stgs.
W.W.

Cl.

mf

p

Angèle

M' - sieur, how glad I am, I need-ed no dis-sua - sion!

RENE

on this fes-tive oc - ca - sion!

Ah,

pp

ANG.

A husband in a — case like this

RENE

mine, at last, the sin — gle bliss a ma — rried man de - serves

Solo
Fl.

p

mf

p

Count of Luxembourg

66

Count of Luxembourg

7

RENE: hate-ful to say "Fare — well".

rit. Cello Solo

Molto rit.

8 Valse moderato

ANG: Tell me, can this be love, sec-ret and strange and new,

RENE: Tell me, can this be love, sec-ret and strange and new,

8 Valse moderato

Harp Stgs.

ANG: Two fool-ish peo — ple, all un-a-ware, caught in a dream come

RENE: Two fool-ish peo — ple, all un-a-ware, caught in a dream come

Count of Luxembourg

72

12 Valse moderato

ANG. bright ro — mance falls from — a - bove, a poor rain damp - ened roc - ket.

ANG. So keep your wed - ding ring, my love, safe in your waist - coat

13 Valse moderato

ANG. poc - ket!

Basil She'll go here, he'll go there, what a strange love af - fair, all the

Pavlovitch She'll go here, he'll go there, what a strange love af - fair, all the

Mentchikoff She'll go here, he'll go there, what a strange love af - fair, all the

Pelegrin She'll go here, he'll go there, what a strange love af - fair, all the

Valse moderato

but, why the devil did I let them talk me into it....?

15 Moderato

Renè

It's hard to un-der-stand, I on-ly

touched her hand... no – thing more

to ex-plore. Smooth as a

sil – ken glove, soft as a trem – bling dove,

Count of Luxembourg

Count of Luxembourg

78

Count of Luxembourg

23 Tempo di Marcia

RENÉ
rich a - gain, this cheque of mine quite plain - ly guar - an - tees it, the moment's come to—

RENÉ
dine and wine, and I pro-pose to seize it, no mat-ter what the sum may be, some

RENÉ
fool-ish fel - low's paid me! I'll spend the lot most happ-i - ly, with friends like you to

RENÉ
aid me! I call up on each var - let, to paint the cit - y scar - let! This

Count of Luxembourg

Act II

No. 9. OPENING

(Angèle and Chorus)

Allegro molto

The Entrance Hall of Angele's House

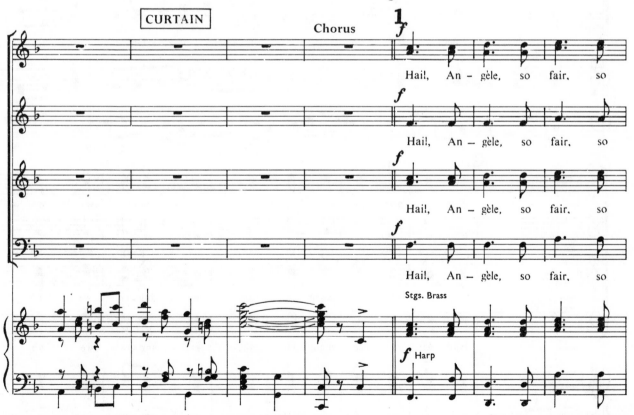

Hail, An – gèle, so fair, so

Hail, An – gèle, so fair, so

Hail, An – gèle, so fair, so

Hail, An – gèle, so fair, so

88

ANG.
to - night I sang a last fare - well...   **Chorus**

We lose you,   dar - ling
We lose you,   dar - ling
We lose you, our dar - - ling
Vln.   We lose you, our dar - - ling

ANG.
So   Fate de - crees...   I   leave at

CHO.
dem - oi - selle?
dem - oi - selle?
dem - oi - selle?
dem - oi - selle?   Solo Vln.

4

ANG.
last   the world   of paint and pow - der,   the dream world   where I've

Fl.

Count of Luxembourg

Count of Luxembourg

8 Chorus

Ah ____ Ah ____

Ah ____ Ah ____

One day I shall find po - et - ic words to fill my

One day I shall find po - et - ic words to fill my

TUTTI

I shall find, shall find po - et - ic words, and the mel - o - dy so di - vine ____ will

I shall find, shall find po - et - ic words, and the mel - o - dy so di - vine ____ will

mind ____ and the mel - o - dy so di - vine ____ will

mind ____ and the mel - o - dy so di - vine ____ will

all be mine!

all be mine!

all be mine!

all be mine!

9 Vivo ANGÈLE: Thank you, dear friends, this is the last you are going to see of Angele Didier.

9 Vivo Stgs.

Count of Luxembourg

94

GUESTS: Oh, no, Angèle, please...   ANGÈLE: Of Angèle Didier, the opera singer, who gave   her last performance tonight.

Give me a chance however, and in a moment or two Angèle Didier, your hostess, will join you at supper in the winter garden ! *(Cheers)*

10

CHO.

So An - gèle your fai - ry tale finds a ro - man - tic en - -

So An - gèle your fai - ry tale finds a ro - man - tic en - -

So An - gèle your fai - ry tale finds a ro - man - tic en - -

10 So An - gèle your fai - ry tale finds a ro - man - tic en - -

CHO.

- ding, and in our hearts we en - vy so the one who set your heart a - glow. _____

- ding, and in our hearts we en - vy so the one who set your hear a - glow. _____

- ding, and in our hearts we en - vy so the one who set your heart a - glow. _____

- ding, and in our hearts we en - vy so the one who set your heart a - glow. _____

Count of Luxembourg

No. 10. MAZURKA
(Ballet)

Cue: I feel it—ouch!—in my bones! Juliette—!

Count of Luxembourg

3 Meno

Coda

No. 11. DUET
(Angele and Rene)

CUE: Ridiculous and altogether impossible

RENE: dreams has filled my fuddled brain___ dreams that will still be mine, when I'm a-

1 Valse moderato

RENE: - wake !

2 Angèle

Have a care, a dream can be but flee — — ting, so be - ware

ANG. of hearts too wild - ly bea — — ting, love that's born in one brief hour of

ANG. mad — ness, with the dawn may fly a - way, leave on - ly sad-ness

rit.

3 a tempo

ANG. Love's a star that fool-ish mor-tals sigh for, all the world's

Rene
Love's a star that fool-ish mor-tals sigh for, all the world's

ANG. un - hap - py chil-dren cry for... glitt'-ring star, a fan-cy sent to

RENE un - hap - py chil-dren cry for... glitt'-ring star, a fan-cy sent to

ANG. blind you... Ah ___ may nev-er find you, love's a dream!

RENE blind you... Ah ___ may nev-er find you, love's a dream!

4 Animato

RENE No, An-gèle, you are wrong, no, for dreams are but the kind of truth

Count of Luxembourg

Count of Luxembourg

Allegretto

ANG.

I've heard e-nough of that old star-ry stuff of fan-cies and dreams and ro-

ANG.

-mance, my prac-ti-cal mind says I'm like-ly to find something still in the thrill of a

6 **Valse**

ANG.

dance...

Rene

I still have, it seems, my

Girls (SOPRANI, ALTI)

(off-stage, bouche fermée) Mm ____ mm ____ mm

6

Vlns.

RENE

faith in dreams and in my heart I find your

GIRLS

mm

Cello Hn.

8 Valse moderato

one smile ten-der and proud, de-clared, my dream-ing was true,___

one smile ten-der and proud, de-clared, my dream-ing was true,___

molto rit.

___ My heart whis-pered a-loud "My love, dear love, is you"___

___ My heart whis-pered a-loud "My love, dear love, is you"___

molto rit.

They dance ever more closely to each other

9 **a tempo**

Cello Solo

Solo Vln.

10 Stgs.

ANGÈLE *breaks away.* RENÉ: Angèle, what's the matter?

ANGÈLE: Baron, we should never have met . . . never spoken . . . or danced !

RENÉ: But, Angèle, I love you, I want to marry you !

ANGÈLE: Marry me? That would be impossible - you see - I am married already !

ANGÈLE *(hiding her face - exit)*

No. 11a. ENTRANCE OF DANCERS

No. 12. "LIP TO LIP" DUET
(Juliette and Brissard)

CUE: Well then, here it comes

arms do not tease, tell me please just why? _____ You're so

Juliette

-ress had a thrill I can't still ex - plain! _____ I can't

Brissard

1

cool, so cor - rect, Say "po - lite," say "dis - creet." That has just no ef -

Brissard   **Juliette**

wait to re - sume It was gay, it was grand. Oh, your frag - rant per -

Juliette   **Brissard**

-fect Here's my heart at your feet That is no use at all to a

Brissard   **Juliette**

-fume Oh, your wan - der - ing hand As a start it was worth all of

Juliette   **Brissard**

girl at a ball Now I've seen what you mean, I'll try.

Brissard

hea - ven on earth Now we know, let it go a - gain!

Juliette

Count of Luxembourg

JUL.

Ah

BRIS.

When a ro mance has once be gun, dan cing is some thing

JUL.

Ah

That was

BRIS.

more than fun.

Count of Luxembourg

No. 13. "THE ROSEBUD AND THE BEE"

(Basil and Girls)

CUE: An old bumble bee in a garden of roses

1. Once a ho — ney bee came bum-bling to a
2. When she heard his Bum — ble mutt -'ring in his

rose bud young and fair _____ Rose-bud heard him shy - ly
bold and bee like bass _____ Rose-bud said with pet - als

mum-bling "My de - vo - tion I de - clare _____ Lit - tle
flutt -'ring "If I yield to your em - brace _____ Will you

Count of Luxembourg

Count of Luxembourg

116

Count of Luxembourg

No. 13a. MELOS

CUE: ... bought and sold poor little Paulette

Allegro

No. 14. THE GLOVE SONG
(Rene)

CUE: This will be my only souvenir of a disastrous adventure

122

Attaca No. 14a

Count of Luxembourg

No. 14a. MAZURKA - REPRISE

No. 15. "RAZZLE-DAZZLE BASIL"
(Basil and Juliette)

CUE: The most tempestuous terpsichorean west of Vladivostok!

5 Molto Allegro

No. 16. FINALE ACT II
(Full Company)

CUE: ...within an inch of his life

RENE: Now what the devil's this?

Allegro

ff Tpts.

TUTTI

DIALOGUE UP TO (JULIETTE)

...from your dancers at the opera Tempo di Valse

ff TUTTI

Count of Luxembourg

Count of Luxembourg

1 Meno

Count of Luxembourg

Count of Luxembourg

DIALOGUE UP TO . . . consented to become my wife !

4 Moderato   LADIES : Congratulations, Angèle . . .

Vln. pizz.
Stgs.

CUE : So let me make a small confession !

Count of Luxembourg

Our wedding day was a ro-man-tic af - fair he hard-ly not-iced that I was

Hell!

there!

He went right, miles a-

She went left, miles a-

-part day and night,

-part day and night, something one might well dis - par - age...

In that most un-us -ual

RENÉ

- get me nev - er! More than my name I sold you

RENÉ: *(Spoken)* And that no one can give me back, I sold you my heart's happiness!

RENÉ

dear, far more...

Allegro   RENE *(turns to go, ANGÈLE runs after him)*   Presto

14

TUTTI *f*

ANGÈLE: No, Rene, no, It can't end like this. Remember that I am your wife!   RENÉ: Angele, my darling love.
BASIL: This is outrageous!

15 Moderato
Angèle

That fool - ish wed - ding day I was in Hea - ven then

Count of Luxembourg

16 Allegro non troppo

Act III
No. 17. "THE CHAMPAGNE CALL"
(Saville and Guests)

Molto Vivo

The Champagne Garden of the Grand Hotel

3 Dance (a la Can-Can)

4

Count of Luxembourg

Count of Luxembourg

150

Count of Luxembourg

CHO.

bright time will be had by all if you just ans-wer the cham-pagne call!

bright time will be had by all if you just ans-wer the cham-pagne call!

bright time will be had by all if you just ans-wer the cham-pagne call!

bright time will be had by all if you just ans-wer the cham-pagne call!

11 Tempo primo

Dance (a la Can-Can)

Count of Luxembourg

No. 18. REPRISE
(Saville, Marchand and Juliette)

Allegretto

Saville: A great lit-tle game, la Vie de Bo-heme, for those who care!

Marchand: Your stud-i-o's got a patch of dry-rot from here to there!

Juliette: Oh, what a bed: The mat-tress was burst, 'cause the mice had a home there first _____

All Three

rit.

And if those days came back a new, we'll tell you what we'd do ____ We'd

Brass

Tempo di Marcia

JUL.
SAV.
MAR.

dash through the door - way and rush down the stair, life in a poor way's a

JUL.
SAV.
MAR.

loath some af - fair! Art may be art and love en – dure, but

JUL.

who wants to live on the Rue d'A - mour! _____ And

SAV.
MAR.

who wants to live on the Rue d'A - mour! We'd dash through the door way and

Count of Luxembourg

No. 18a. ENTRANCE OF PRINCESS

Cᴜᴇ: It's all yours, Brissard

a la Marcia Festivo

No. 18b. MELOS

CUE: JULIETTE AND BRISSARD *exeunt*

Valse moderato

Count of Luxembourg

No. 19. "FIRST LOVE"

(The Princess, Angèle and René)

CUE: I am not too old to remember *that!*

Count of Luxembourg

PRINCESS: all at once ____ you are grown up ____ in the sweet - ness ____ and com-

PRINCESS: -plete - ness ____ of that won - der - ful first love. ____

2 Piu Vivo

PRINCESS: Eyes shin-ing like stars ____ and the touch of a wand - 'ring

PRINCESS: hand ____ and the first shy words all young

3

PRINCESS: lo - vers un - der - stand. ____ Ah, the warm, ling - 'ring

Count of Luxembourg

162

Count of Luxembourg

No. 20. FINALETTO
(Angele, Rene and Chorus)

CUE: So you two gentlemen are friends?

Count of Luxembourg

Count of Luxembourg

No. 21. FINALE ASSOLUTO
(Full Company)

Count of Luxembourg

Count of Luxembourg

Count of Luxembourg

170

Count of Luxembourg

Count of Luxembourg